Are We Nearly There Yet?

© Text copyright Carol Davenport.
Designed by Jonathan Sanderson and Jack Challoner.
ISBN: 978-0-9954750-8-3
First published in Great Britain in 2019 by Explaining Science Publishing.

Are We Nearly There Yet?

Carol Davenport

Rosie is a robot rover.

Here she is, flying high in the
sky, tucked up safely in
her spaceship.

1

Rosie should be asleep, but a storm on the surface of the Sun has woken her up.

"Don't worry, Rosie, it's just a storm," says Mission Control, all the way from Earth.

"Go back to sleep now."

Rosie tries to sleep.

She really tries.

Very quietly, she asks:

"Are we nearly there yet?"

4

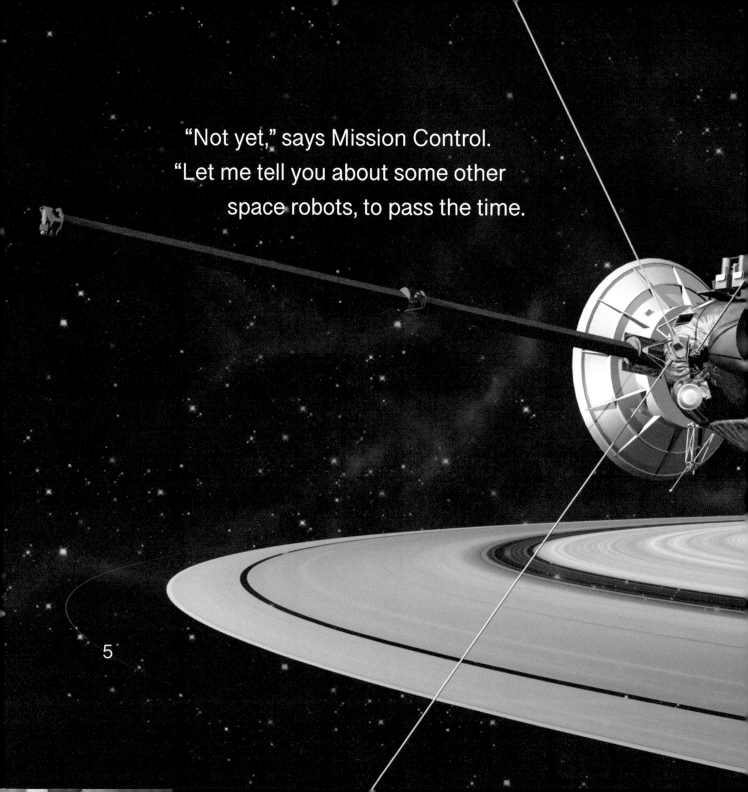

"Not yet," says Mission Control.
"Let me tell you about some other
space robots, to pass the time.

5

Here are Huygens and Cassini.
They flew to one of Saturn's
moons, called Titan."

"Huygens braved the
winds of Titan, and
made it to the ground.

Titan is a cold, cold world
with lakes of liquid gas."

7

"Cassini stayed high above,
listening for Huygens and
sending messages back to Earth.

Then Cassini danced through
the rings of Saturn."

"How beautiful,"
whispers Rosie,
and she dreams of
dancing as she flies
to Mars.

10

Later ...

"Are we nearly there yet?"

"Not yet, Rosie.

I'll tell you about more space robots.

Here are Rosetta and Philae.

They chased a comet, caught it,
and joined it on its lonely journey
around the Sun."

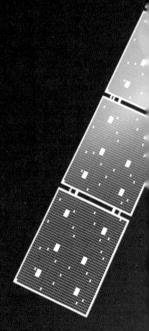

"Philae bounced and landed on the comet.
Sniffed the surface.

13

Then Rosetta landed there too,
to keep the comet company
in the depths of space."

"How kind," whispers Rosie,
and she dreams of chasing comets
as she flies to Mars.

Later ...

"Are we nearly there yet?"

"Not yet, Rosie.

Let me tell you about
New Horizons, racing to
the edge of the Solar System."

"New Horizons passed Pluto in a flash.

Sent back pictures to the Earth.

Kept on flying, ever further."

17

"How fast," whispers Rosie, and she dreams of racing
as she flies to Mars.

Later ...

"Are we nearly there yet?"

"Not yet, Rosie.
Here are the twins,
Spirit and Opportunity.

They went to Mars, too.

19

They each landed in a ball of balloons.

Two rovers exploring Mars, testing the soil,
mapping the hills."

"How bouncy," whispers Rosie,
and she dreams of balloons
as she flies to Mars.

Later ...

"Are we nearly there yet?"

"Not yet, Rosie.
Here is Curiosity.
Another rover. Roaming Mars.
Finding out what Martian rocks are made of.

21

Curiosity is still working
hard, sending back
information
to Earth ...

... driving around,
snapping selfies."

"How smart," whispers Rosie,
and she dreams of cameras
as she flies to Mars.

Later ...

"Are we nearly there yet?"

"Very nearly, Rosie. Soon you will be at Mars.
Then you will leave your spacecraft and fly down ...

... to take photos of things never seen.

To dig deeper than any other rover.

To sniff for signs of ancient life.

To explore."

24

"How exciting," whispers Rosie. "How exciting."

Rosie's real name is Rosalind Franklin. This is what she will look like when she reaches Mars in 2023. She'll look for evidence that simple life might have existed there, long ago.

This is actually the European Space Agency's previous Mars spacecraft. Rosie's ship will probably look similar when it launches in 2022. The 'wings' are solar panels.

The Huygens lander is tucked behind the cone-shaped cover under its spacecraft, Cassini. In January 2005 Huygens was dropped into the atmosphere of Titan, one of Saturn's moons, testing the gases on its way to the surface.

The Rosetta spacecraft, with its lander Philae, was launched in 2004. Ten years later it caught a comet called Churyumov-Gerasimenko, and Philae landed on the comet. Two years after that Rosetta also landed, taking some final measurements before shutting down.

Before the New Horizons spacecraft visited, our best view of Pluto was a blurry smudge taken by telescopes. Now we've seen features and detail which will help us work out how Pluto was formed. New Horizons is now on its way to other rocky objects on the outer edge of our Solar System.

Spirit and Opportunity are twin rovers which landed on opposite sides of Mars in January 2004. They were supposed to work for three months, but Spirit kept going for six years and Opportunity is still operating more than ten years later!

This selfie was taken on 5th August 2015 by Curiosity, which has a camera on a long boom. Several pictures were pasted together to assemble this photo. The rover is studying the Martian climate and geology.

For more information on each mission featured in this book, see: nustem.uk/space

How to use this book.

I hope that you enjoy reading the book with a child. Doing science is all about asking questions – something that children are also very good at.

The scientists that worked on the different space missions in this book did not know the answers to their questions, and so they designed the robots to help find out answers.

Encourage your child to think about what it might be like to be on different planets. You could help them to build their own Rosie the Rover using toy blocks. Imagine how the surface of the different planets and space objects might be.

If your child asks a question that you don't know the answer to, don't worry. To enjoy science you don't have to know the right answers, you just have to be willing to ask questions that might help find out the answer.

Carol Davenport

Image credits

p.18: 'Pluto dazzles in false colour'. NASA/JHUAPL/SwRI.

p.19: 'Opportunity' (artist's impression, on Mars). NASA/Jet Propulsion Laboratory-Caltech.

p.20: 'Emerging' (artist's impression of Spirit, on Mars).
NASA/Jet Propulsion Laboratory-Caltech.

pp.21-22: 'Curiosity Self-Portrait at 'Mojave' Site on Mount Sharp' (Mars). NASA/JPL-Caltech/MSSS. Note: MSSS = Malin Space Science Systems, San Diego, who made the Mars Hand Lens Imager (MAHLI) camera at the end of the robot arm.

Pages 27-28: 'Closer Mars', showing Mars in the night sky, used under Creative Commons Attribution-ShareAlike 2.0. Photo by Flickr user 'the real Kam75'.

p.32: Artist's impression of Earth and Moon, public domain photo by Pixabay user PIRO4D.

Acknowledgements

This book originated as part of NUSTEM's Family Space Explorer project, which was funded by the UK Space Agency. The author wishes to thank Northumbria University for continued support.

Thanks also to Bruce Davenport for his original idea of a not-very sleepy rover on her big adventure, and to Jonathan Sanderson for the initial design.

Explaining Science Publishing collaborates with working scientists and science writers as well as poets, artists and illustrators, to create books that aim to explain scientific and mathematical ideas and inspire scientific thinking.

Want to know more? Check us out at www.explaining-science.co.uk